COLLEGE DAYS

BY STEPHEN LEACOCK

39955

NEW YORK
DODD, MEAD AND COMPANY
1924

PRINTED IN THE U. S. A. BY
The Quinn & Boden Company
BOOK MANUFACTURERS
RAHWAY   NEW JERSEY

Preface

I present this little book to such of the public as care to read it, without apology. The "pieces" that are included in it appeared in bygone years in the Toronto *Varsity*, the McGill *Outlook*, the Harvard *Advocate*, the Princeton *Tiger* and other journals of the same uncommercial and ideal character. The responsibility for their existence rests with the brilliant and uncalculating young men who are editors of such publications.

I am aware that some of these sketches and verses are local and topical in their nature. But I have lived and breathed so long in a college atmosphere that I am convinced that all colleges are in a measure alike, and that what is said of one is true of all.

Many of the men whose names appear here in print are now numbered with the majority. I trust that it is no violation of good taste to leave any mention of them unaltered from what it was. I have no other intention than to honour their memory.

STEPHEN LEACOCK.

Contents

MY COLLEGE DAYS: A RETROSPECT

My College Days: A Retrospect

WHEN I look back upon the men and things of my college days and compare them with the college days of those who are now undergraduates, I stand appalled at the contrast.

What strikes me most in looking back to the college life of my time is the extraordinary brilliance, the wonderful mental powers of the students of those days. In my time there were men at college, especially in the year above me, who could easily have discovered, had they cared to, the Newtonian Laws of Motion and the Theory of Light.

This, I think, was particularly noticeable in the very year when I happened to be a freshman. The fourth year, the graduating class, of that moment represented a galaxy of intellectual capacity which was probably unparalleled in the history of the human mind. I state this in posi-

3

tive terms because I myself witnessed it. I
knew, or at any rate, I saw and heard, these
very men. It will always remain with me as a
source of gratification till I die, that it was my
lot to enter college at the very time when the
fourth year represented an exaltation of the
intellect never since equalled.

The deplorable change which has since happened was already, I fear, setting in during my
own college days. The third year and the second year men, when they came to graduate, al-
though infinitely in advance of anything I have
since known, stood for a range of mentality far
below that of the first graduating class that I
remember. More than that, I am compelled to
admit that the classes which followed immediately upon my own year were composed of the
very dregs of the human intelligence and be-
tokened an outlook and a point of view more
fitted for the nursery than the class room. Nor
is the change that I observe only in the students.

The professors whom I see about me to-day,
ordinary, quiet men, with the resigned tran-
quillity that betrays the pathos of intellectual

4

failure,—how can I compare them with the intellectual giants to whom I owe everything that I have forgotten. The professors of my college days were scholars,—vast reservoirs of learning into whose depths one might drop the rope and bucket of curiosity—to bring it up full to the brim with the limpid waters of truth. Plumb them? You couldn't. Measure their learning? Impossible. It defied it. They acknowledged it themselves. They taught—not for mere pecuniary emolument—they despised it—but for the sheer love of learning. And now when I look about me at their successors, I half suspect (it is a hideous thought) that there is a connection between their work and their salaries. Nor is it only a change in the students and the professors.

The old place itself—my Alma Mater—how it has altered.

Is this the great campus that I remember so well from my freshman days? What was it? Half a mile long, I think, and broader even than its length. That football goal that stood some fifty or sixty feet in the air, has it shrunk to these poor sticks? These simple trees, can they be the great elms that reared themselves up to the autumn sky? And was the Tower no higher then than this?

Nay, Fate, that hath given me so much, that hath brought to me my lettered degrees, and my academic standing with its comfortable license to forget—wilt thou not take it all back again and give me in return by some witchery of recollection—one hour of the Brave Old Days Beyond Recall.

MY MEMORIES AND MISERIES
AS A SCHOOLMASTER

My Memories and Miseries as a Schoolmaster

FOR ten years I was a schoolmaster. About thirty years ago I was appointed to the staff of a great Canadian school. It took me ten years to get off it. Being appointed to the position of a teacher is like being hooked up through the braces and hung up against a wall. It is hard to get down again.

From those ten years I carried away nothing in money and little in experience; indeed, no other asset whatever, unless it be, here and there, a pleasant memory or two and the gratitude of my former pupils. There was nothing really in my case for them to be grateful about. They got nothing from me in the way of intellectual food but a lean and perfunctory banquet; and anything that I gave them in the way of sound moral benefit I gave gladly and never missed.

But schoolboys have a way of being grateful. It is the decent thing about them. A schoolboy, while he is at school, regards his masters as a mixed assortment of tyrants and freaks. He plans vaguely that at some future time in life he will "get even" with them. I remember well, for instance, at the school where I used to teach, a little Chilean boy, who kept a stiletto in his trunk with which he intended to kill the second mathematical master.

But somehow a schoolboy is no sooner done with his school and out in the business of life than a soft haze of retrospect suffuses a new colour over all that he has left behind. There is a mellow sound in the tones of the school bell that he never heard in his six years of attendance. There is a warmth in the color of the old red bricks that he never saw before; and such a charm and such a sadness in the brook or in the elm trees beside the school playground that he will stand beside them with a bowed and reverent head as in the silence of a cathedral. I have seen an "Old Boy" gaze into the open door of an empty classroom and

ask, "And those are the same old benches?"
with a depth of meaning in his voice. He has
been out of school perhaps five years and the
benches already seem to him infinitely old.
This, by the way, is the moment and this the
mood in which the "Old Boy" may be touched
for a subscription to the funds of the school.
This *is* the way, in fact, in which the sagacious
head master does it. The foolish head master,
who has not yet learned his business, takes the
"Old Boy" round and shows him all the *new*
things, the fine new swimming pool built since
his day and the new gymnasium with up-to-date
patent apparatus. But this is all wrong.
There is nothing in it for the "Old Boy" but
boredom. The wise head master takes him
by the sleeve and says "Come"; he leads him
out to a deserted corner of the playground and
shows him an old tree behind an ash house and
the "Old Boy" no sooner sees it than he says:

"Why, Great Cæsar! that's the same old tree
that Jack Counsell and I used to climb up to
hook out of bounds on Saturday night! Old
Jimmy caught us at it one night and licked us

both. And look here, here's my name cut on the boarding at the back of the ash house. See? They used to fine us five cents a letter if they found it. Well! Well!"

The "Old Boy" is deep in his reminiscences, examining the board fence, the tree and the ash house.

The wise head master does not interrupt him. He does not say that he knew all along that the "Old Boy's" name was cut there and that that's why he brought him to the spot. Least of all does he tell him that the boys still "hook out of bounds" by this means and that he licked two of them for it last Saturday night. No, no, retrospect is too sacred for that. Let the "Old Boy" have his fill of it, and when he is quite down and out with the burden of it, then as they walk back to the school build-ing, the head master may pick a donation from him that falls like a ripe thimbleberry.

And most of all, by the queer contrariety of things, does this kindly retrospect envelop the person of the teachers. They are transformed by the alchemy of time into a group of profound scholars, noble benefactors through whose teaching, had it been listened to, one might have been lifted into higher things. Boys who never listened to a Latin lesson in their lives look back to the memory of their Latin teacher as the one great man that they have known. In the days when he taught them they had no other idea than to put mud in his ink or to place a bent pin upon his chair. Yet they say now that he was the greatest scholar in the world and that if they'd only listened to him they would have got more out of his lessons than from any man that ever taught. He wasn't and they wouldn't—but it is some small consolation to those who have been schoolmasters to know that after it is too late this reward at least is coming to them.

Hence it comes about that even so indifferent a vessel as I should reap my share of schoolboy gratitude. Again and again it happens to me that some unknown man, well on in middle life, accosts me with a beaming face and says: "You don't remember me. You licked me at Upper Canada College," and we shake hands with a warmth and heartiness as if I had been his earliest benefactor. Very often if I am at an evening reception or anything of the sort, my hostess says, "Oh, there is a man here so anxious to meet you," and I know at once why. Forward he comes, eagerly pushing his way among the people to seize my hand. "Do you remember me?" he says. "You licked me at Upper Canada College." Sometimes I anticipate the greeting. As soon as the stranger grasps my hand and says, "Do you remember me?" I break in and say, "Why, let me see, surely I licked you at Upper Canada College." In such a case the man's delight is beyond all bounds. Can I lunch with him at his Club? Can I dine at his home? He wants his wife to see me. He has so often told her about having been licked by me that she too will be delighted.

I do not like to think that I was in any way brutal or harsh, beyond the practice of my time, in beating the boys I taught. Looking back on it, the whole practice of licking and being licked, seems to me mediæval and out of date.

14

Yet I do know that there are, apparently, boys that I have licked in all quarters of the globe. I get messages from them. A man says to me, "By the way, when I was out in Sumatra there was a man there that said he knew you. He said you licked him at Upper Canada College. He said he often thought of you." I have licked, I believe, two Generals of the Canadian Army, three Cabinet Ministers, and more Colonels and Majors than I care to count. Indeed all the boys that I have licked seem to be doing well.

I am stating here what is only simple fact, not exaggerated a bit. Any schoolmaster and every "Old Boy" will recognise it at once; and indeed I can vouch for the truth of this feeling on the part of the "Old Boys" all the better in that I have felt it myself. I always read Ralph Connor's books with great interest for their own sake, but still more because, thirty-two years ago, the author "licked me at Upper Canada College." I have never seen him since, but I often say to people from Winnipeg, "If you ever meet Ralph Connor—he's Major

15

Charles Gordon, you know—tell him that I was asking about him and would like to meet him. He licked me at Upper Canada College."

But enough of "licking." It is, I repeat, to me nowadays a painful and a disagreeable subject. I can hardly understand how we could have done it. I am glad to believe that at the present time it has passed or is passing out of use. I understand that it is being largely replaced by "moral suasion." This, I am sure, is a great deal better. But when I was a teacher moral suasion was just beginning at Upper Canada College. In fact I saw it tried only once. The man who tried it was a tall, gloomy-looking person, a university graduate in psychology. He is now a well-known Toronto lawyer so I must not name him. He came to the school only as a temporary substitute for an absent teacher. He was offered a cane by the college janitor whose business it was to hand them round. But he refused it. He said that a moral appeal was better: he said that psychologically it set up an inhibition stronger than the physical. The first day that he taught—it was away up in a little room at the top of the old college building on King Street—the boys merely threw paper wads at him and put bent pins on his seat. The next day they put hot beeswax on his clothes and the day after that they brought screw drivers and unscrewed the little round seats of the classroom and rolled them down the stairs. After that day the philosopher did not come back, but he has since written, I believe, a book called "Psychic Factors in Education"; which is very highly thought of.

But the opinion of the "Old Boy" about his teachers is only a part of his illusionment. The same peculiar haze of retrospect hangs about the size and shape and kind of boys who went to school when he was young as compared with the boys of to-day.

"How small they are!" is always the exclamation of the "Old Boy" when he looks over the rows and rows of boys sitting in the assembly hall. "Why, when I went to school the boys were ever so much bigger."

After which he goes on to relate that when

he first entered the school as a youngster (the period apparently of maximum size and growth), the boys in the sixth form had whiskers! These whiskers of the sixth form are a persistent and perennial school tradition that never dies. I have traced them, on personal record from eye-witnesses, all the way from 1829 when the college was founded until to-day. I remember well, during my time as a schoolmaster, receiving one day a parent, an "Old Boy," who came accompanied by a bright little son of twelve whom he was to enter at the school. The boy was sent to play about with some new acquaintances while I talked with his father.

"The old school," he said in the course of our talk, "is greatly changed, very much altered. For one thing the boys are very much younger than they were in my time. Why, when I entered the school—though you will hardly believe it—the boys in the sixth form had whiskers!"

I had hardly finished expressing my astonishment and appreciation when the little son came back and went up to his father's side and started whispering to him. "Say, dad," he said, "there are some awfully big boys in this school. I saw out there in the hall some boys in the sixth form with whiskers."

From which I deduced that what is whiskers to the eye of youth fades into fluff before the disillusioned eye of age. Nor is there need to widen the application or to draw the moral.

The parents of the boys at school naturally fill a broad page in the schoolmaster's life and are responsible for many of his sorrows. There are all kinds and classes of them. Most acceptable to the schoolmaster is the old-fashioned type of British father who enters his boy at the school and says:

"Now I want this boy well thrashed if he doesn't behave himself. If you have any trouble with him let me know and I'll come and thrash him myself. He's to have a shilling a week pocket money and if he spends more than that let me know and I'll stop his money altogether." Brutal though this speech sounds, the real effect of it is to create a strong prejudice in the little boy's favor and when his father curtly says, "Good-bye, Jack," and he answers, "Good-bye, father," in a trembling voice, the schoolmaster would be a hound indeed who could be unkind to him.

But very different is the case of the up-to-date parent. "Now I've just given Jimmy fifty dollars," he says to the schoolmaster with the same tone as he would to an inferior clerk in his office, "and I've explained to him that when he wants more he's to tell you to go to the bank and draw for him what he needs." After which he goes on to explain that Jimmy is a boy of very peculiar disposition, requiring the greatest nicety of treatment; that they find if he gets in tempers the best way is to humour him and presently he'll come round. Jimmy, it appears can be led, if led gently, but never driven. During all of which time the schoolmaster, insulted by being treated as an underling (for the iron bites deep into the soul of every one of them), has already fixed his eye on the undisciplined young pup called Jimmy with a view to trying out the problem of seeing whether he can't be driven after all.

But the greatest nuisance of all to the schoolmaster is the parent who does his boy's home exercises and works his boy's sums. I suppose they mean well by it. But it is a disastrous thing to do for any child. Whenever I found myself correcting exercises that had obviously been done for the boys in their homes I used to say to them:

"Paul, tell your father that he *must* use the ablative after *pro*."

"Yes, sir," says the boy.

"And, Edward, you tell your grandmother that her use of the dative case simply won't do. She's getting along nicely and I'm well satisfied with the way she's doing, but I cannot have her using the dative right and left on every occasion. Tell her it won't do."

"Yes, sir," says little Edward.

I remember one case in particular of a parent who did not do the boy's exercise but, after letting the boy do it himself, wrote across the face of it a withering comment addressed to me and reading: "From this exercise you can see that my boy, after six months of your teaching, is completely ignorant. How do you account for it?"

I sent the exercise back to him with the added note: "I think it must be hereditary."

In the whole round of the school year, there was, as I remember it, but one bright spot— the arrival of the summer holidays. Somehow as the day draws near for the school to break up for holidays, a certain touch of something human pervades the place. The masters lounge round in cricket flannels smoking cigarettes almost in the corridors of the school itself. The boys shout at their play in the long June evenings. At the hour when, on the murky winter nights, the bell rang for night study, the sun is still shining upon the playground and the cricket match between House and House is being played out between daylight and dark. The masters—good fellows that they are— have cancelled evening study to watch the game. The head master is there himself. He is smoking a briar-root pipe and wearing his mortar board sideways. There is wonderful greenness in the new grass of the playground and a wonderful fragrance in the evening air. It is the last day of school. Life is sweet indeed in the anticipation of this summer evening.

If every day in the life of a school could be the last, there would be little fault to find with it.

LAUS VARSITATIS: A SONG IN PRAISE OF THE UNIVERSITY OF TORONTO

Laus Varsitatis: A Song in Praise of the University of Toronto [1]

(*Varsity War Supplement*, 1916)

NO one, I think, can blame me if I want to
    Exalt in verse the University of Toronto.
I always do, I hope I always will
Speak in the highest terms of Old McGill;
That institution, I admit with tears,
Has paid my salary for sixteen years.
But what is money to a man like me?
Toronto honoured me with her degree.

O Seat of Learning, at whose Norman Gate
My feeble steps learned to matriculate,
O ancient corridors and classrooms dim,
That youth that once you sheltered, I am him.

[1] It would be false modesty to conceal the fact that this poem was submitted for the Chancellor's Gold Medal. It didn't get it.

Ghosts of departed decades, wake and see,
That boy in the short trousers. I am he.
And after thirty years I bring along
This unsolicited return of song.

Roll back the years, O Time, and let me see
The College that was Varsity to me;
Show me again those super-sylvan spots
Now turned to choice suburban building lots.
Spread wide the trees and stretch the park afar,
Unvexed as yet by the electric car,
Till once again my listening ear shall seize
The Taddle murmuring beneath its trees
And Fancy see in that far yesterday
The Bloor Street farmers hauling in their hay.

Thus at fond memory's call as through a haze
I see the men and things of other days.
Dim shades appear within the corridor
And noiseless footsteps fall upon the floor.
Lo! Noble Wilson—dared we call him Dan?
Musing, the while, on Prehistoric Man,
Draw nearer still, O Venerable Shade,
Read me that lecture on the Third Crusade,

28

Let thy grave voice its even tenor keep,
Read it again.   This time I will not sleep.

Profound in thought, melodious in tongue
I seem to see thee still, O Paxton Young,
How gladly I would ask thee, if I could,
One or two points I never understood.
You said one day that all our judgments were
Synthetically *a priori,* sir,—
I never doubted it, I never will.
I thought so then and I believe it still,
Yet whisper low into my ear intent
What did you say that *a priori* meant?

But see these shadowy forms, so strange yet
    like,
That head!—'tis Chapman—and that brow—
    'tis Pike.
That coloured chalk, that moving hand, that
    bright
Description of the Neurilemma—Wright,
That voice within the room—pause here and
    listen—
Mittel Hoch Deutsch—it is, it's Vandersmissen.

O Noble Group! what learning!   There were
    some
Possessed a depth one hardly dared to plumb,
Others a width of superficies that
Makes the professors of to-day look flat.
And all are gone, departed, vanished, nil—
Called to the States or summoned further still,
Some have resigned, or been dismissed, or died,
Others, while still alive, Carnegified,
And in their stead their soft successors play,
In flannelled idleness at Go-Home Bay.

All gone?   Not so, some still are on the ground
Fraser is with us still, and Squair is round,
Still Hutton's Attic wit the classroom pleases
And Baker keeps at least as young as Keys is.
Others there are—*j'en passe et des meilleurs*—
Who still recall to us the days that were.

For those were days of Peace.   We heeded not.
Men talked of Empire and we called it rot;
Indeed the Empire had no further reach
Than to round out an after-dinner speech,

Or make material from which John A.
Addressed us on our Convocation Day.
There was not in the class of '91
A single student who could fire a gun.
Our longest route march only took us—well,
About as far as the Caer Howell Hotel,
Our sole protection from aggression lay
In one small company—its number K.

O little company, I see thee still
Upon the campus at thine evening drill.
Forming in fours, with only three in line,
A target for such feeble wit as mine.
All honour to the few who led the way,
Barker and Coleman, Edgar and McCrae,
Geary, Ruttan, and Andy Eliot, who
Is now dispensing justice at the Soo,
And Ryckert—let me pause and think of him,
Is it conceivable he once was slim!
And, yes, perhaps the most important one
Friend of my youth, good Howard Ferguson
The kindest man that ever failed to pass
In First Year Trigonometry, alas!—

This man of place and power, has he forgot
His boyhood friend? Oh, surely, he has not!
When next some well-paid sinecure you see
O Howard, pass it, pass it on to me.

A noble band, these veterans of K.
Born out of time, living before their day,
Paying their own expense, their belts, their
        boots,
And calling ever vainly for recruits.
O K, thou wert O. K., but not to be,
And sank as sinks a raindrop in the sea,
Yet from thine ashes—if a raindrop can
Be said to have such things—there they began
A mighty movement, and one well may say,
You put the K in Canada to-day.

For see, the Past has gone! It fades apace
And the loud, angry Present takes its place,
Lurid and red and shaken with alarms,
The thunder that proclaims a world in arms,
What sounds are these, O Varsity, that fall
Loud on thy corridors, the bugle call,

The muster roll, the answering cry, the drum,
As from thy quiet halls thy students come,
O ancient corridor! soft fall the light
Upon their hurrying faces, brave and bright,
Children they seemed but yesterday and then
As in a moment they are turned to men.
Hush low the echoes of thy stone-flagged floor,
Footsteps are passing now that come no more.

And they are gone! The summer sunshine
  falls
Through the closed windows of thy silent halls,
The winter drags its round, the weary spring,
And the slow summer still no tidings bring
Of their return. Yet still, O Gateway Gray,
Silent but hopeful thou dost wait the day—

And it shall come. Then shall the bonfires burn
To tell the message of their glad return.
Ho, porter, wide the gate, beat loud the drum,
Up with the Union Jack, they come, they come!
Majors and Generals and some V.C.'s—
Had ever college such a class as these?

33

Let the wine flow—excuse me, I forgot—
I should say, in Ontario, let it not,
But let at least the pop be strongly made
And more than lemons in the lemonade.
Let the loud harp and let the mandolin,
In fact, let any kind of music in—
And while the wildest music madly whirls,
Why, then—if I may say it—bring the girls.
And under circumstances such as these
Come, give them all gratuitous degrees.

And there are those who come not, but for them
We sing no dirge, we chant no requiem.
What though afar beneath a distant sky
Broken and spent, shall their torn bodies lie,
And the soft flowers of France bloom once
    again
Upon the liberated soil above the slain
Who freed it, and her rivers lave
As with their tears the unforgotten grave,
Whilst thou, O land of murmuring lake and
    pine,
Shall call in vain these vanished sons of thine—

They are not dead. They shall not die while
    still
Affection live and Memory fulfil
Its task of gratitude. Nor theirs alone
The sculptured monument, the graven stone;
The Commonwealth of Freedom that shall rise
World-wide shall tell their noble sacrifice.

THE OLDEST LIVING GRADUATE

The Oldest Living Graduate

I FIND him wherever I go among the colleges,—the *Oldest Living Graduate*. At every College Reunion, there he is; at each Commencement Day you may expect him among the first,—a trifle bent he is and leans, one cannot but note it, somewhat heavily upon his stick; and there is something in his eye, a dimness, a far-away look as of one to whom already a further horizon is opening.

Yet, frail or not, he is there among the graduates at the earliest call. The younger men may hesitate about a hundred mile journey to attend the Annual Dinner of the Alumni,—not he. The younger men may grudge the time or count the cost,—not so the oldest living graduate.

See, it is Commencement Day. There sits the Oldest Living Graduate in the very foremost row of the seats in the college hall. His hand is bent to his ear as he listens to the President's farewell address to the graduates. But he hears no word of it. His mind is back on a bright day in June,—can it be sixty years ago?—when first he heard the like of it.

Easy and careless he was then, the Youngest Living Graduate, happy in his escape from the walls of the Temple of Learning. A butterfly, he was, hatched from his silken skeins and glorying in the sunshine.

The gaze of the Youngest Living Graduate was turned forwards, not back. He was looking out upon life, eagerly and expectantly. For the time being the sights of the grounds of the campus had faded from his eye and ear. His mind was bent, his strength was braced, to meet the struggle of the coming years. It is the law of life. He had no time, as yet, for retrospect, and in his very eagerness was overcareless of the things that lay behind.

But as the years slipped past the ties of memory began to tighten in their hold. There was time, here and there, in the struggle of life, for a fleeting glance with the past. And lo! How soft the colour that began to lie on the pictured vision of his college days. The professoriate, once derided, how wise they seemed. It is ever their hard lot to be honoured only when they are dead; but all the greater is the honour. The glory of the campus, the football game played into the November dusk, —how the shouts of it will linger in the ear of memory when half a century has gone. Nay, even the lamp of learning itself, how softly now does it illuminate the long neglected page; and the brave lettering of the degree, what a fine pride of forgotten knowledge does it now contain! And, my friends, you and I and each of us were once the youngest, or at least the latest living graduate. The time is coming, if we stay to see it, when we shall be the oldest. The time is coming when you and I and an ancient group that we still call our "Class," will walk the green grass of the campus on Commencement Day with the yearning regret for all that we might have done; with the longing for lost opportunity that is the chief regret of Age.

While there is time, let us be up and doing. Before yet we are the oldest living graduate, let us borrow something of the spirit that inspires him. Let us discount a note against the future with Father Time and receive its value in the glowing coin of present affections. While our class yet live let us realise what a splendid group they are; and let us find the opportunity to tell the professors how much we owe to them before we write our gratitude upon their tombstones. And if our college wants our support, our help, and our enthusiasm, let us bring it forth with all the affection of the Oldest Living Graduate and with all the power and eagerness of the youngest.

THE FACULTY OF ARTS

The Faculty of Arts

DEAR Mr. Dean, I think it much com-
           pleter,
       To voice to-night my sentiments
           in metre,
This little thing—I ask your blessing on it—
   Is what we technically call a sonnet.
Sonno, I sing and Nitto, I do not,
   A derivation made upon the spot.

Here let me interject to save confusion,
   There has not been the very least collusion,
I had not given any intimation
   That I intended such an innovation,
And if you find my verses poor and mean,
   Worthy professors, do not blame the Dean.
For years I have dissembled, now you know it,
   My friends! behold in me an unknown poet

[1] Verses written for Dean Moyse's dinner to the Professors of the Faculty of Arts, McGill University, October 29, 1909.

Careless of notoriety, of fame unthinking.
  But singing like a skylark after drinking.
So, tasting this good cheer from soup to Stilton,
  I can't remain a mute inglorious Milton.
Let every man pursue his different way
  And seek his life work where he finds his pay.
I leave to Walker gas, to Caldwell Kant,
  Adams the rock; Penhallow keeps the plant,
Let the bacilli stay where they belong.
  But leave to me the humble joy of song.

A sonnet, did I say? Nay, I confess
This is an epic neither more nor less,
Arts and the Men, I sing, for I am yearning,
To sound the praise of Academic learning.

How start the theme with teeming fancies
      fraught,
How measure into feet the crowding thought,
How mark the rhythm and divide the time
And bid the stubborn syllables to rhyme,—
  In other words, how can I jam it, sir,
  In Petersonian Pentameter?

First, let me voice a wish I must avow
    The Board of Governors might see us now.
That we might have to make the tale complete,
    An Angus and a Greenshields, and a Fleet.
Oh, sirs, this spectacle would make them feel
    That poor professors like a solid meal,
That learning, since it is no hollow sham,
    Looks best with a distended diaphragm.
Well may they boast among their employees,
    A group of smiling faces such as these!
Yet 'tis a theme on which I must not touch,
    In fairness be it said we owe them much,
And let us hope the future has in store
    That one and all shall shortly owe them
        more.
Yes, let me voice this humble, earnest plea,
    Participated by this company—
When next the stream of benefaction starts,
    Pray, pour it on the Faculty of Arts!
O Edward, William, Robert, James, and John,
    Delay no longer, kindly turn it on!

For this the Faculty of Arts is known,
Of other studies the foundation stone,

It forms the base, however deeply hid,
Of higher education's pyramid.

Let medicine discourse in cultured tone,
Of pickled corpse and desiccated bone,
Yet let it answer, if it dares to speak,
Who taught it how to name the bones in
    Greek?

Or let the scientist pursue his toil,
   Grease his machines with lubricating oil,
Fling far the bridge and excavate the mine.
   And bid the incandescent light to shine,
Yet let him answer—will he dare to tell,
   Who tries to teach the engineer to spell?

Or let the law, if proof be needed yet,
   To our great Faculty deny its debt,
The Latin it must use to mystify,
   Is raw material that we supply.
The logic that Dean Walton takes his tricks on
   Is manufactured by Professor Hickson.

But I have said enough, I think, to show
   The debt of gratitude all others owe

To this our Faculty. Now let me come
  To details lying rather nearer home.
And let me speak about the various parts
  That constitute this Faculty of Arts,
This done with your permission I will then
  Say something of our most distinguished
    men.
And with all gentleness I will assign
  To each a brief Thanksgiving Valentine.

Here first the Classics holds its honoured
    place,
  The centre stone of the aforesaid base,
In education's whirling stream and jam,
  It lies embedded like a cofferdam.
So deeply down do its foundations lie,
  Its worth is hidden from the common eye.
The vulgar think the classics are a sham,
  O noble edifice, O Greek, O dam!
Yet judge its worth when you can find them
    beaten,
  Messrs. Macnaughton, Peterson and Eaton,
See where Macnaughton with imperious tread,
  Rudely disturbs the archæologic dead,

49

Watch him receive in his extended hat
    The venal offering of the plutocrat.
Watch this, my friends, and will you dare to
      say
    The study of the classics does not pay?

Or see, a Peterson with spade and hoe
    In ducal vaults exhumes a Cicero!
Carries it gently to the outer air,
    Wipes off the dust with Caledonian care,
And straightway to the classics is annexed
    A new and highly controversial text,
A noble feat! and yet, alas! I own,
    Like Dr. Cook he did it all alone,
When next in search of Cicero you go,
    Take, Mr. Principal, an Eskimo.

Lo! Mathematics hidden from the view,
    Behind its symbols though it may be true,
The upper part of it so wrapped in darkness,
    That no one sees it but Professor Harkness.
The very Queen of Sciences they say!
    It is, for the professor, anyway.

In lectures he is not obliged to talk.
    Needs but a blackboard and a bit of chalk,
A set of problems given as a test
    Then down he sits—the students do the rest;
Forgive me if I fall into ecstatics,
    Would I were taught to teach the Mathe-
        matics!

Charming as is the mathematic mystery,
    It will not stand comparison with history,
Imagine what a splendid tour de force,
    To trace the Norman Conquest to its source,
Think of a man who still quite young was
        skilled
    To analyse the Mediæval Guild!
To follow it and trace its rootage down
    Deep buried in the Anglo-Saxon town!
Yet such is Colby! Oh, what joy complete
    To terrorise the man upon the street.
To hush his crude attempts at conversation
    By quoting pages of the Reformation,
And that his cup of misery be filled,
    To crush him with the Mediæval Guild.

51

O Charles, with all thy knowledge is it right
    That thou art not beside the board to-night?
That thou shouldst set thy brain to overplan
    The simple, unsuspecting business man!
See! at the bidding of the gentle sage
    The Caligraph creeps noiseless o'er the page
The clatter of the noisy keys is dumb
    Destroyed by Colby's patent Liquid Gum.
O second Gutenberg, God speed the ship
    That bears you on your European trip,
Let bulky Germans drink your health in hock,
    And frantic Frenchmen clamour for the stock
And, Noiseless Charles, when you have had
        your fill
    Of business life, come back to fond McGill.

Surely no nobler theme the poet chants
    Than the soft science of the blooming plants.
How sweet it were in some sequestered spot
    To classify the wild forget-me-not;
To twine about the overheated brow
    The coolness of the rhododendron bough;
To lie recumbent on a mossy heap
    And draw a salary while fast asleep.

Dr. Penhallow, it would need a Herrick
  To sing your work and that of Carrie
      Derick,
Nor shall my halting Muse in vain essay
  Such sweet co-operation to portray.

Would that your time allowed you once or
      twice,
  To drink to Barnes, discoverer of ice!
All unsuspected in the river bed
  The tiny frazil reared its dainty head.
No one had known for centuries untold
  Why the Canadian climate was so cold.
Why winter should be vigorous and rude
  In such a truly Southern latitude.
Barnes, after years of thought and anxious
      teasing,
  Decided that there must be something freez-
      ing.
He stopped his lectures, bundled up his
      pack,
  Braved untold hardships at the Frontenac,
And then, within a stone's throw of Quebec,
  Found ice that no one ventured to suspect.

Let ice and snowdrift sing their requiem,
   Our Howard Barnes is going to settle them.
A fairer prospect opens to the eye!
A Canada beneath a sultry sky!
   Already the prophetic eye of hope
Sees grapevines circle the Laurentian slope
   Palms and pomegranates with the breezes
      play
And luscious figs droop over Hudson Bay.

Last but of all departments valued most,
   Is that illuminated by our host,
English! the very word inspires the thought
   With memories of a noble nation fraught.
English, the tongue of Tennyson, of Gray,
Of Milton, Bunyan, Goldsmith, Pope and Gay
Of still more widely circulated names
   Of Henty, E. P. Rowe and G. P. James,
The tongue of Bobbie Burns and Walter Scott,
   You interrupt me?—strictly it was not.
But let me tell you, sirs, who dares to fight it?
   Let Saxons speak it but let Scotsmen write it!
English, to add to this enumeration
   The tongue to-day of every place and nation

For cultured Chinaman, for wild Hindoo,
  For travelling Russian nothing else will do.
The tongue of every race and every clan
  Just think how needful to a gentleman!
Varied as are the forms of English speech
  Our dean has got his solid grip on each,
Here sits a man who positively knows
  The whole life history of our nation's prose.
Who can, and will, at your request rehearse
  One thousand lines of Anglo Saxon verse.
To him, we feel it in his every look,
  Chaucer and Gower are an open book
He finds the verse of Cædmon light and breezy
  And Beowulf, if anything, too easy,—
Nay, bless, my soul, the man can even read
  The jargon of the Venerable Bede.

Yet not for this, or not for this alone
  We love to claim him as our very own,
Rich in the scholar's gift in every part
  Yet more we prize the richness of his heart
The cheerful humour nothing can dismay
  Unruffled by the cares of day to day.

The industry that does not flag or shirk,
 That stints not trouble, measures not its
  work.
The kindness never failing and the hand
 Outstretched to help, the brain to under-
  stand
With ready sympathy another's cares
 And lighten thus the burden that it shares,
O sirs, if this in English may be sought
 Would that such English were more widely
  taught.
Let him recite us Cædmon if he will
 Or sing us Beowulf, we will be still;
Nay, let him quote us, if he feel the need,
 Whole chapters from the Venerable Bede.
Still shall we cry the pauses in between
 God's blessing on our well-beloved Dean.

ENGLISH AS SHE IS TAUGHT AT COLLEGE

English as She Is Taught at College

IT is an amazing fact, but it is nevertheless true, that Mr. Rudyard Kipling or Sir James Barrie, or, let us say, ex-President Eliot of Harvard, would fail hopelessly in English if they tried to pass the entrance examination of any American or Canadian University. King George, from whom presumably the King's English flows as from its fountain source, might get perhaps halfway through a high school in the subject.

As for Shakespeare, I doubt if he knew enough of what is called English by our education departments to get beyond a kindergarten. As to passing an examination on one of his own plays, such as is set by our colleges for matriculation, he couldn't have done it; he hadn't the brains,—at least not the kind of brains that are needed for it.

These are not exaggerations, they are facts. I admit that when the facts are not good enough, I always exaggerate them. This time they don't need it.

Our study of English—not merely in any one state or province, but all over North America, except in happy Mexico—begins with years and years of the silly stuff called grammar and rhetoric. All the grammar that any human being ever needs, or that is of any use as an intellectual training, can be learned in a few weeks from a little book as thin as a Ritz-Carlton sandwich. All the rest of the solid manuals on the subject is mere stodge. It serves no other purpose than to put royalties into the pockets of the dull pedants who elaborate it.

Rhetoric is worse. It lays down laws for the writing of sentences and paragraphs about as reasonable and as useful as a set of directions telling how to be a gentleman, or how to have a taste for tomatoes.

Then comes English Literature. This is the

last stage, open only to minds that have already been debilitated by grammar and rhetoric.

We actually proceed on the silly supposition that you can "examine" a person in English literature, torture it out of him, so to speak, in the course of a two hours' inquisition. We ask him to distinguish the "styles" of different authors as he would the colour of their whiskers. We expect him to divide up authors into "schools" and to sort them out as easily as a produce merchant classifies fish.

The truth is that you cannot examine in English in this way, or only at the cost of killing the very thing that you wish to create. The only kind of examination in the subject I can think of would be to say to the pupil, for example, "Have you read Charles Dickens and do you like it?" and when he answered that he didn't care for it, but that his uncle read it all the time, to send a B.A. degree to his uncle.

We make our pupils spend about two hours a day for ten years in the silly pursuit of what we call English, and yet at the end of it we wonder that our students have less real appreciation of literature in them than when they read a half-dime novel for sheer artistic joy of it.

THE LENGTHENING OF THE
COLLEGE COURSE

A Little Glimpse into the College Future [1]

THE president, in his valedictory address, spoke with deep feeling, and was frequently interrupted by the sobs of the graduating class. They had now been together, he said, more years than he cared to count. They had come together as young men; they had spent the energetic years of their middle age together in these venerable halls, and now, when with advancing old age it had become absolutely necesssary that they should graduate before they died, he felt that it was hard indeed to part. He could not but contrast on this occasion the organisation of the college and the new meaning which graduation from Harvard had acquired with the almost unbelievable condition of

[1] Harvard Commencement Day of 1950. Current Press Report of the President's Speech to the Graduating Class.

things which he could recall as actually existing in his youth. In those days men graduated from the university after perhaps no more than eight or nine years of study. He himself had actually seen a Harvard degree given to a man —a brilliant man, he admitted—who had spent only six years at the college. Under such conditions education was necessarily slipshod and incomplete. It was customary, as he remembered, for men to go no further in Conic Sections than page 150: as to what came after page 150 there had prevailed a regrettable indifference. He was glad to say that he could see men seated before him this morning who had done the entire book. (*Applause.*) In earlier days students were allowed to go out of Harvard knowing something of plain trigonometry but absolutely ignorant of spherical. (*Groans and sobs.*) No such man could get out now. (*Renewed groans.*) He himself, and he said it with emphasis, would rather keep a man at Harvard till he died than send him out adorned with the college degree yet ignorant even of the simplest spherical formulæ. (*Applause.*) Such a thing was unfair to the graduates themselves. They went out into the business world ignorant and ill equipped. They fell an easy prey to the rapacity of the business man. No such thing, he ventured to say, could happen to-day.

In continuation the president said that he was assured that any one of the venerable gentlemen seated before him in the graduating class would meet with nothing but respect and consideration during his life in the outside world. His life might indeed be short. That he would not deny. But it would, he hoped, be full. (*Applause.*) Experience had taught him that it was better to be short and full than not to be. In conclusion, he congratulated the venerable gentlemen before him on their long and sustained acquirement of knowledge. He could see men in front of him who had learned in their Latin Grammar not *some* of the irregular verbs, but *all* of the irregular verbs. There were men before him who knew what came after the first book of Xenophon's Anabasis: men who had read not one Canto

of Dante's Inferno, but all of it: who had read
and appreciated not merely a part of English
literature, but the whole of it. This, he said,
was education indeed. He did not wish to
keep the class seated too long and he would
gladly request some of the older members to
lie down if they wished to do so. But he
would like to detain them and the audience
long enough to invite· their consideration of
the question as to why a Harvard man should
ever graduate. (*Applause.*) This question,
he was pleased to say, was being earnestly
debated by the corporation. Funds would
probably be available within a short time to
render graduation unnecessary, and to keep the
Harvard men of the future at College until
removed by death. The increasing comfort of
the dormitories, the continued improvement of
the food in the college halls, together with the
fearful rise of the cost of living in the outside
world and the spread of Bolshevism and other
dangers, rendered this reform more and more
desirable. He felt that in turning these venerable gentlemen out into the cold world, the

college was performing an ungrateful task. He shuddered to think of what might happen if a Bolshevist should get hold of one of them. The corporation was engaged, however, in looking round for new things that could be studied. It was felt that there must be something left if one could only find it. In conclusion he would like to ask the audience to step out quietly as he observed that some of the senior graduates were asleep.

A SUBSCRIPTION WITH REFLECTIONS

A Subscription with Reflections [1]

THE enclosed seventy-five cents, like all other money, speaks for itself. If *The Rebel* goes on as it has begun I am sure it will have no difficulty in knocking the public out of their seventy-five cents's. To me *The Rebel* came as a real enlightenment. I realised that I had been, without knowing it, a rebel for thirty years past; in fact ever since the time when I sat on the benches of University College and speculated on men and things with the same irresponsible freedom that *The Rebel* shows to-day. I found, if I remember rightly, much to criticise and much to alter. In fact the whole college of those days seemed gradually subsiding, for want of a little active interference on my part,

[1] The reflections which are here given were occasioned by my having to subscribe seventy-five cents to a new students' journal.

into the mud of its own foundations. I found, too, upon diligent enquiry, that this same situation has existed before, very notably indeed, in the generation of the older graduates; in fact had existed and persisted and seemed to follow the good old college like a ghost; the ghost, if one had to name it, of Academic Discontent that has moaned and wrung its hands at the gates of colleges and academies from the time of Plato to the age of Theodore Roosevelt. It is credibly reported (I believe I have it from Professor Hutton) that in Plato's later days his students used to gather in little knots among the trees of his Academy, and shake their heads at the kind of "dope" that Plato was "putting over" in his lectures. It had, they said, no "punch." And it is equally strongly affirmed that the students of Aristarchus of Samos denounced his theories of lunar motion as "chestnuts"; that the students of Marsiglio of Padua were openly heard to avow that "the old man was going 'batty'"; that the students of Sir Isaac Newton at Cambridge said that they were "simply sick" of hearing about gravitation with the same old joke each year about the apple; that the students of Adam Smith at Glasgow said that if he could only cut out his everlasting "division of labour" for a lecture or two and get down to common sense, they might listen to him. Nay, worst of all, I have seen students in the back of my own classroom shake their heads and murmur that my lectures are "bum stuff" to what they used to be.

Yet I have grown to know that out of the empty breath of discontent is blown the inspiration of the future. And I have ceased to regret that academic discontent should be. On the contrary I am even inclined, as a professor, to harbour a little bit of academic discontent of my own. Discontent, perhaps, is a word a trifle too strong; in the quiet and regulated life of a professor no passion as strong as that can find a place; for the life of a professor passes from middle age to seniority and from seniority to senility with the measured and majestic transit of the harvest moon passing over the ripened field of corn, and mellowing all that it illuminates. But if ever a professor could voice a wish for a change in the methods or aspect of universities I may say that it often occurs to me that our colleges would be greatly brightened if there were no students; if the professors could saunter undisturbed among the elm trees in friendly colloquy, lecturing—for they know no other form of conversation—to one another; if the library and the campus could enjoy at all seasons the quiet hush that now only falls on them in August; if the deep peace where learning loves to brood were never broken by examinations and roll-calls—and— dear me, I see that I am unconsciously falling into poetry; suppose that I loop the loop clear into it and continue:

"Ah, that the peace where learning loves to brood
  Were never broken by the student rude,
  And that the corridor and classroom dim
  Sheltered the prof. but quite excluded *him!*
  Thus the professor, free from every care,
  Might settle down in comfort on his chair,
  And while the noiseless years in gentle current flow
  Pursue profound research or, better, let it go."

Let me in conclusion draw your attention to the elegance of the introduction of that Alexandrine couplet at the end of the verse, a neat trick which I had of my instructors at University College thirty years ago.

TORONTO AND McGILL

Toronto and McGill [1]

(1913)

THE object of this poem is not very
difficult to get onto,
Since it is intended all through as what
is called a poem on Toronto.
I don't deny, have not and never will
My debt of gratitude to old McGill
Nor have I any other wish or hope
Than here upon Mount Royal's leafy slope
To theorise, to formulate conjectures,
In short to give the kind of thing called lectures
Here live, here die and after,—who can tell,
To go on giving lectures up in ———[2]

---

[1] This poem was composed in celebration of a great
football victory of these two colleges over one another.
It is written in what is now called *vers libre*. But in my
college days we used to call it worse than that.

[2] Word apparently missing.—Editor.

Let me explain at once for those who do not
    know 'em,
The kind of metres, called gas metres, which
    I use in this poem.
Anybody with a quick ear will have no doubt
    from the very start
That it must be a most extraordinarily difficult
    kind of art.

Each foot begins and ends just where I end or
    begin it,
I defy any man to scan it, though it might be
    possible to skin it
But even the combined strength of Dr. Peter-
    son and Mr. Slack
Could tackle one of these verses and throw it
    on its back.
But as I say, I want to sound the praise,
Of old Toronto, long may be her days.

You taught me all I know, O good old College,
Greek, Latin, Algebra, Religious knowledge,
Fondly and freely gave it all away,
And made me at the end of it B.A.

You taught me Greek, can I forget it? No!
I've tried to, but it simply will not go.
Still in my dreams my wayward thoughts in-
    cline,
Irregular exceptions to decline;
And up and down my midnight fancies go
To the strange rhythm of α ὁ, ἡ, To.

When my declining years preclude extension,
I'll end in an irregular declension.

Toronto, you taught me Latin, yes, you did,
I have the marks, the thing cannot be hid.

Deep in the fibre of my brain is sunk
The furrow of *hic haec hoc hujus hunc*
I bear the marks of Virgil and the scar
Where Julius Cæsar wrote his Gallic war.
Horatius Flaccus stamped me with his verse
And Cicero: I don't know which was worse.

'Twas cruel while it lasted, it is done:
Through this I learned to use my mother
    tongue.

You taught me mathematics, let it pass,
How could you know I was a hopeless ass?
You tried in vain my intellect to hem
Inside the harsh binomial theorem.
I tried my best, no one can say I wouldn't,—
Learned what I could and copied what I
   couldn't.
This too was while it lasted very rotten
But now, thank God, forgiven and forgotten.

But what I chiefly hope will some day save me
Were the instructors that you nobly gave me
McGill may boast her Peterson, her Slack,
Rose and Macnaughton, standing back to back
For such instructors care I not a button
My mind, good sirs, was fashioned by a Hut-
   ton!

McGill may have in history her Fryer,
And her sagacious Colby still is by her,
I grant them merit; it is very strong,
Their history is all right, but mine was Wrong!

Or would you speak of French? You would
  not dare,
For all of mine was taught me on the Squair.

Or if you boast of German, pause and listen,
I had my dose direct from Vandersmissen.

Yet in my humble self I like to think
I typify a sort of missing link,
The phrase is ill-advised, I simply mean
I constitute a sort of go-between.
Trained at Toronto, nurtured by McGill
I know not which should my affection fill.
Backward and forward my affection goes,
One gave me knowledge, one supplies my
  clothes.

One knew me as a gentle silly youth
Eager for learning, passionate for truth
Deep in philosophy, immersed in Greek,
Looking for mental trouble, so to speak.

The other as a teacher of the young,
Prosing on economics all day long

Pent in a little classroom giving notes
And stuffing theory down students' throats,—
Nor visible regard for truth whatever
And yet as young and sillier than ever.

Yet if I do thus form a missing link
I am but one of several, I think.
I do not stand alone, will any man,
Refuse to lift his hat to our Ruttan?
Toronto gave him; may her name be blest
In giving him she gave us of her best.
Nor he alone! Will some one kindly say
What thinks the universe of John McCrae.
That he's all right! I thank you from my soul.
Toronto numbers him upon her roll.

They may thus stand united, side by side,
McGill and Varsity—with each its pride,
Let games like this one we have seen to-day
A double glory to the world display.
Where emulation struggles void of spite,
And men who play the game shall guard the
        right.
If it were possible a toast to fill,
I'd give you, Friends, TORONTO AND McGILL.

86

THE CHILDREN'S CORNER

The Children's Corner [1]

(1902)

OUR good friend, the Editor of this magazine, had some fears that it might suffer by very reason of its excellence; that it might be bowed down by the weight of erudition it contains and become top-heavy with learning. Now this is as grave an ailment as can well threaten any publication, for it acts directly on the circulation. Knowing the editor's apprehensions we have ventured to suggest to him that possibly a hypodermic injection of some lighter matter near the back of the cover might be advisable. He has therefore permitted us to variegate this issue by the addition of a Children's Corner for College Boys and Girls. For the insertion of such a column we are convinced we need

[1] This little essay was written as a contribution to a newly established and very learned college magazine. It was intended to put life into it. The magazine died.

offer no apology to our young friends. Even in the cultivated mind of the college graduate, —cultivated indeed by the years of diligent rolling, harrowing, planting, and possibly ploughing, at the hands of his tutors and examiners,—it is often found that the wheat of wisdom is not unmixed with the chaff of childishness.

As soon then as we had conceived the idea of a Children's Corner, we set about thinking what we could put into it. We decided that the very best thing we could have to begin with would be a lot of letters from our little friends who have graduated, treating of some topic not too exacting on the intellect. This we know to be the usual method of eliciting interest in the Children's Corners of Saturday journalism. So we sent them all a circular which we felt sure would draw; we couched it in the following couching:—

"Dear Sir,—Please write to the Editor of the McGill Children's Corner and state your personal experience of the value of a college education. Speak freely of yourself, but don't get delirious over it. Limit yourself, if you can, to a thousand words, and never write to us again. Send five dollars with your manuscript, and the Editor promises to make use of it."

The results obtained from our circular have been eminently satisfactory; indeed we have received so many bright little letters that we are able to print only a small proportion of them. Here is our first example. It is from "little Charlie," aged 29, a graduate with double first class in English and Metaphysics, now doing splendidly in a position of great trust in a saw mill.

"Dear Mr. Editor,—I am glad you are asking a lot of college boys to write to you. I think a college training is a great help. I have found English invaluable and use nothing else. I must now close."

The next is similar.

"Dear Mr. Editor,—I graduated not long ago and am only twenty-two, but I feel very old. I took Archæology and Sanskrit. Our course of reading in Sanskrit was the Vishnubuddayat, Part one, Book one, Page one. We also scanned the first three lines and examined the skins under the microscope. I don't think anything could have developed my mind quite in the way that Sanskrit and Noah's Archæology have. I owe a lot to my teachers and mean to pay them back some day. Since I took my degree I have got a job opening gates at a railway crossing, and am doing well, as I have just the touch required. When I get a little older I may get a job at a tollgate."

So many thanks for your bright little letter, Teddie, and be sure not to let us hear from you from time to time. You forgot your five dollars, careless boy.

Here is a writer who signs himself Rev. Willie Weekshanks, aged thirty:

"Dear Mr. Editor,—I think a college education is a very valuable thing, and I wish I had had one instead of taking Theology. I liked my college life so much and I revered all my professors. I used to take exact notes of everything they told me, exactly as I remembered it a week afterwards. If need be I could produce my notes before a . . ." (Hush, hush, Willie, please don't talk of anything so painful as producing your notes. Surely, my dear little boy, we have had trouble enough.)

Here is a letter from an Honour graduate in Classics:

"Dear Mr. Editor,—I took Classics. For my part I think at least certainly on the one hand that a college education, especially indeed Greek develops the faculty of thinking, writing and quoting; on the other hand, with less lack of not saying nothing than anything. A man with a full knowledge of Latin and Greek feels himself a 'pons asinorum,' and in the hours of weariness and discouragement can always turn to his education as a delightful 'reductio ad absurdum.' "

But let us pass on to some of the other features of our Children's Corner. Not to be in anyway behind our great contemporaries in journalism, we hasten to present a Puzzle Competition. It is constructed on the very latest models. The puzzles are indeed somewhat difficult and elaborate, but we confidently in-

vite all college children, both graduate and undergraduate, to try them. Come on, then, here
is our first. It is called, THE BURIED WORD:

LAERTNOM

There! try and guess it! The letters of the
above word if spelt backwards will produce the
name of a Canadian city. Sit down now and
work at it; if you don't get the solution at
once, keep at it. To any McGill graduate or
undergraduate sending a correct solution, accompanied by five dollars, we will forward a
copy of the *McGill Calendar*.

Our second puzzle. This is for some of our
little mathematical friends. It is called a double acrostic:

McG*LL

On inserting a vowel in place of the above *,
the word will become the same word that was
the word before the vowel removed was removed. Any one finding the correct solution
will forward us three dollars; on the receipt
of each three dollars the competition is de-

clared closed,—as far as that competitor is concerned.

Our final puzzle. It consists in a historical prize competition, for which we propose the following:

Name the four Georges, giving reasons, and sending four dollars.

OUR HOME STUDY CIRCLE

We had hoped to supplement our Puzzle Department with another feature which is its invariable accompaniment, and which we thought especially appropriate for a College Magazine. This is the Home Study Circle. It is one of the noblest and most philanthropic developments of the modern journal. The admirable facilities for learning offered by these Home Study Circles, with the gratuitous examination papers and short lectures that accompany them, cannot fail to be highly estimated. By this means any man whose affairs have never given him leisure for academic instruction may pick up in the course of, say, ten years, a fair knowledge of Persian or Syriac, enough, that is to say, to make himself easily misunderstood. Indeed, with the help of such a Home Study course, any intelligent boy or girl with a keen desire to add something to his ordinary studies may very quickly lose it. We had therefore begun to prepare a short Home Study Course in higher German philosophy. Our aim was to come to the help of people who were anxious to familiarise themselves with the ideas of some of the great German thinkers (Kant, Schopenhauer, Pilsener Lager, Wiener Schnitzel, etc., etc.), and yet who were unable to get a knowledge of these ideas either from their writings or from the criticisms on them, or through prayer for direct intervention. Unfortunately, difficulties of a technical nature, which need not here be explained, have prevented us from completing our course.

INDOOR GAMES

From the somewhat heavy subject that we treated in our last paragraph we turn with pleasure to present to our readers a sample of one of the new "Indoor Games for College Students" that we hope soon to give to the world. It is called

INDOOR FOOTBALL, or FOOTBALL WITHOUT A BALL.—In this game any number of players, from fifteen to thirty, seat themselves in a heap on any one player, usually the player next to the dealer. They then challenge him to get up, while one player stands with a stop-watch in his hand and counts forty seconds. Should the first player fail to rise before forty seconds are counted, the player with the watch declares him suffocated. This is called a "Down" and counts one. The player who was the Down is then leaned against the wall; his wind is supposed to be squeezed out. The player called the referee then blows a whistle and the players select another player and score a down off him. While the player is supposed to be down, all the rest must remain seated as before and not rise from him until the referee by counting forty and blowing his whistle announces that in his opinion the other player is stifled. He is then leant against the wall beside the first player. When the whistle again blows the player nearest the referee strikes him behind the right ear. This is a "Touch," and counts two.

We cannot, of course, in this place attempt to give all the rules in detail. We may add, however, that while it counts two to strike the referee, to kick him counts three. To break his arm or leg counts four, to kill him outright is called Grand Slam, and counts one game.

There are so many interesting things that we are most eager to insert in this Children's Corner that we fear the limited space at our disposal will not allow us to treat them all. In the interest, however, of our fairer readers, we cannot well refrain from introducing one or two short extracts from our new "College Girls' Cookery Book."

1. Receipt for Latin Paste.

Take one pound of Bradley's "Arnold," a little fluent extract of Virgil, some strong stems and roots. Grind well and soak. Let the mixture stand till it forms into a thick paste, which may be used for all kinds of Latin composition. It will be found an agreeable relish in quotations and does well for public speeches if mixed with a little ginger. The paste is admirably suited for quotations in after dinner speaking if well soaked in alcohol.

2. RECEIPT FOR PRESERVED LECTURES
(Crême de Lecture).

First take a lecture. Then boil it down and remove the froth and gas from it by constant stirring. Skim it, strain it through a wet towel and serve hot or cold according to the taste of the examiner.

3. HOW TO MAKE HASH OF AN EXAM. PAPER
(Papier Mâché).

Take a thorough smattering of the subject. Mix it completely in your mind. Spread it very thinly on paper and serve lukewarm. Try to avoid roasting.

We should have been delighted to add a few extracts from our new "Elementary Taxidermy for Students, or How to Stuff Examiners," which we are certain would have made a pleasant feature of our Children's Corner. A few lines from our "Carpentry for College Boys; or how to make German Brackets," would not have been amiss. But we fear we have already trespassed too far on the Editor's kindness.

A SERMON ON COLLEGE
HUMOUR

A Sermon on College Humour [1]

I SHOULD like just for once to have the privilege of delivering a sermon. And I know no better opportunity for preaching it than to do so across the cradle of this infant *Goblin* to those who are gathered at its christening.

As my text let me take the words that were once said in playful kindliness by Charles the Second, *"Good jests ought to bite like lambs, not dogs; they should cut, not wound."* I invite the editors of this publication to ponder deeply on the thought and when they have a sanctum to carve the words in oak below the chimney piece.

The best of humour is always kindly. The worst and the cheapest is malicious. The one is arduous and the other facile. But, like the

[1] This exhortation was addressed to the infant college paper called *The Goblin* of Toronto. *The Goblin* followed my advice, and look at it now.

facile descent of Avernus, it leads only to destruction.

A college paper is under very peculiar temptations to indulge in the cheaper kinds of comicality. In the first place its writers and its readers are for the most part in that early and exuberant stage of life in which the boisterous assertion of one's own individuality is still only inadequately tempered by consideration for the feelings of others.

In the second place it finds itself in an environment that lends itself to the purposes of easy ridicule. The professor stands ready as its victim.

The professor is a queer creature; of a type inviting the laughter of the unwise. His eye is turned in. He sees little of externals and values them hardly at all. Hence in point of costume and appearance he becomes an easy mark. He wears a muffler in April, not having noticed that the winter has gone by! He will put on a white felt hat without observing that it is the only one in town; and he may be seen with muffetees upon his wrists fifty years after the fashion of wearing them has passed away.

I can myself recall a learned man at the University of Chicago who appeared daily during the summer quarter in an English morning coat with white flannel trousers and a little round straw hat with a blue and white ribbon on it, fit for a child to wear at the seaside. That man's own impression of his costume was that it was a somewhat sportive and debonair combination, such as any man of taste might assume under the more torrid signs of the Zodiac.

As with dress, so with manner. The professor easily falls into little ways and mannerisms of his own. In the deference of the classroom they pass unchallenged and uncorrected. With the passage of the years they wear into his mind like ruts. One I have known who blew imaginary chalk dust off his sleeve at little intervals; one who turned incessantly a pencil up and down. One hitches continuously at his tie; one smooths with meaningless care the ribbons of his college gown.

As with his dress, so with the professor's

speech. The little jest that he uttered in gay impromptu in his first year as a lecturer is with him still in his declining age. The happy phrase and the neat turn of thought are none the less neat and happy to him for all that he has said them regularly once a year for thirty sessions. It is too late to bid them good-bye. In any case, perhaps the students, or perhaps some student, has not heard them; and that were indeed a pity.

When I was an undergraduate at the University of Toronto thirty years ago, the noblest of our instructors had said the words *"Hence accordingly"* at the commencement of such innumerable sentences that the words had been engraved by a college joker across the front of the lecturer's desk. They had been there so long that all memory of the original joker had been lost. Yet the good man had never seen them. Coming always into his classroom from the same quarter of the compass, he was still able after forty years to use the words *"Hence accordingly"* as a new and striking mode of thought. The applause which always greeted the phrase he attributed to our proper appreciation of the resounding period that had just been closed. He always bowed slightly at our applause and flushed a little with the pardonable vanity of age.

Having fun over a thing of that sort is as easy as killing a bird on the nest, and quite as cruel.

Can it be wondered, then, that every college paper that sets out to be "funny" turns loose upon the professoriate. It fastens upon the obvious idiosyncrasies of the instructors. It puts them in the pillory. It ridicules their speech. It lays bare in cruel print and mimic dialogue the little failings hitherto unconscious and unknown. And for the sake of a cheap and transitory laughter it often leaves a wound that rankles for a lifetime.

My young friends, who are to conduct this little *Goblin,* pause and beware.

For the essential thing is that such cheap forms of humour are not worth while. Even from the low plane of editorial advantages they are poor "copy." The appeal is too narrow. The amusement is too restricted; and the after-taste too bitter.

If the contents of a college paper are nothing more than college jokes upon the foibles of professors and fellow-students, the paper is not worth printing. Such matter had better be set forth with a gum machine upon a piece of foolscap and circulated surreptitiously round the benches of the classroom.

If the editors of *The Goblin* are wise they will never encourage or accept contributions that consist of mere personal satire. If a student is as fat as the Fat Boy himself let him pass his four years unrecorded in the peace due to his weight. If a professor is as thin as a meridian of longitude let no number of *The Goblin* ever chronicle the fact.

At the end of every sermon there is, so far as I remember, a part of it that is called the benediction. It consists in invoking a blessing upon the hearers. This I do now. I should not have written in such premonitory criticism of *The Goblin,* if I did not feel myself deeply interested in its fortunes. I think that a journal of this kind fills a great place in the life of a university. As a wholesome corrective of the pedantry and priggishness which is the reverse side of scholarship it has no equal. It can help to give to the outlook of its readers a better perspective than the cramped vision induced by the formal pursuit of learning. In the surroundings of your University and your province it has, I think, a peculiar part to play. You are in great need—I hope I say it in all gentleness—of the genial corrective of the humorous point of view. You live in an atmosphere somewhat overcharged with public morality. The virtue that surrounds you is passing—so it sometimes seems to more sinful outsiders—into austerity.

In other words, to put it briefly, you are in a bad way. Your undergraduates, if they were well advised, would migrate to the larger atmosphere and the more human culture of McGill. But if they refuse to do that, I know nothing that will benefit them more than the publication of a journal such as yours is destined, I hope, to be.

A CHRISTMAS EXAMINATION

A Christmas Examination

WITH every revolving year,—and the poets and the physicists agree that they do revolve,—I am struck with the strange inconsistency of the words "Christmas Examination." Here on the one hand is Christmas, good, glad, old season with its holly berries and its lighted candles and its little children dancing in a world of magic round a glittering tree; Christmas with its fabled Santa Claus defying our modern civilisation by squeezing his way down the galvanised iron pipe of a gas grate; Christmas with the sleigh-bells all a-jingle, with bright snow in the streets, with the church-bells ringing on a week day and such a crisp gladness in the air that even the angular faces of university professors are softened out into something approaching human kindliness.

Here, I say, on the one hand is Christmas.

And here on the other hand are Examinations with their sleepless nights and their fevered days, with crazy questions and crooked answers, set with the calculating cruelty of the inquisitor, answered with the patient resignation of the martyr, or with the fanatical frenzy of the devotee who has swallowed his instructor's text book and gone crazy over it;—Examinations with their hideous percentages, their insulting distinctions of rank, and paid for, in cold fees, with money enough to spread a Christmas banquet for the whole university.

Here is Christmas and here are the Examinations. And the two won't go together.

We can't alter Christmas. We've had it nearly two thousand years now. In a changing world its lights glimmer through the falling snow as a quiet beacon on things that alter not. It stands there fixed as a very saturnalia of good deeds, a reckless outbreak of licensed benevolence, with its loosened pocketbooks and smiling faces, just to show us on one day of the year what we might be on the other three hundred and sixty-four,—stands a moment and then passes, leaving us to button about us again our little suit of protective selfishness with nothing but a memory to keep us warm inside.

Christmas we cannot alter. But the examinations, we can. Why not? Why will not some theorist in education tell us how we can infuse into the Christmas examinations something of the spirit of the season that gives them birth? Can we not break down something of these rigid regulations that every candidate reads, shuddering, in the printed instructions on his examination book? Can we not so estimate our percentages and frame our questions?—

And when I had written thus far the whole idea of the thing broke upon me with the flood light of discovery. Of course, nothing simpler, I reached out my hand and drew to me the hideous code of the examination regulations. I read it over with a shudder. Is it possible that for fifty years this university has tolerated such a flat violation of every rule of Christmas behaviour? I saw at once how, not only the regulations, but the very examination papers themselves ought to be so altered that the old malicious spirit might be driven right out of them and Christmas come to its own again even in an examination hall.

Here is the way it is done:

REGULATIONS FOR CHRISTMAS EXAMINATIONS

1. Candidates are permitted—nay, they are encouraged—to enter the examination hall half an hour after the examination has begun, and to leave it, re-enter it, walk across it, jump across it, roll round in it, lie down in it, tear their clothes, mutilate their books and, generally, to make themselves thoroughly and completely at home at the expense of the University.

2. Candidates are not only permitted to ask questions of the presiding examiner, but they may, if they like, talk to him, sing to him, hum grand opera to him in whole or in part, use his fountain pen, borrow his money, and, if need be, for the sake of order, request him to leave the hall. But remember that the presiding examiner is like yourself—a very human

being and, if you had the advantage of knowing him outside the classroom you would find him at this time of year one of the jolliest creatures conceivable.

If you could see him presiding over the little candidates around the Christmas tree in his own house you would almost forgive him that silly dignity which he assumes to cover his natural humanity.

3. Speaking or communicating with every other candidate, male or female, is of course the privilege of every student and the use of the megaphone and gramophone shall in no way be curtailed or abridged.

4. Students may either make use of the books, papers and memoranda provided by the examiner or may bring in their own memoranda, vade-mecums and conundrums together with such dictographs, gramophones, linotypes, stethoscopes or any other aids to memory that they may see fit to use.

5. The plea of accident or forgetfulness will be immediately received, in the same spirit as given.

6. Five per cent will be accepted as a satisfactory standard, but all students failing to obtain it may be, and most certainly will be, specially exempted from further effort by a vote of the Board of Governors.

So much for the regulations. But of course still more can be accomplished if the examiners will only frame their questions to suit the gentle kindliness of the season. I should not wish to show in any great detail how this is to be accomplished. That would be trespassing on the work of departments other than my own. But I may be allowed to point the pathway of reform by proposing a few specimen questions in representative subjects.

CHRISTMAS EXAMINATION IN CLASSICS

1. Who was Themistocles? [*Note. If you can't think it out for yourself, he was a great Roman general, or Greek, or something. The examiner doesn't know much about it himself, but, Lord bless you, at this time of year he doesn't care any more than you do.*]

2. Translate the accompanying passages, or don't bother to, just as you happen to feel about it. After all you must remember that ability to translate a lot of Latin verses is a poor test of what you really are worth.

3. Pick out all the verbs in the above and parse them, or, if you don't feel like picking them out, leave them sticking where they are. Remember that they've been there for two thousand years already.

There! That's the way the Christmas examination in Classics is to be conducted. And in the same fashion one might try to soften down the mathematical examination into something like this:

EXAMINATION IN MATHEMATICS

1. Solve the following equations,—but if you can't solve them, my dear boy, don't worry about it. Take them home to your father as a Christmas present and tell him to solve them. It's his business anyway, not yours. He pays the fees and if he can't solve the equations,

why your family must stand the loss of them. And anyway people ought not to mind the loss of a few equations at Christmas time.

There! That's enough for the mathematical examination. And as for the rest, you can easily see how they ought to be framed.

But just wait a minute before we come to the end. There would remain one examination, just one, that I think every student ought to pass at this season, though he may forget it if he will, as all the kind things of Xmas are forgotten all too soon. I should call it, for want of another name, an Examination in Christmas Kindliness, and I warn you that nothing but a hundred per cent in it can be accepted for a pass. So here it is.

EXAMINATION IN CHRISTMAS KINDLINESS

1. Is the University such a bad place after all?

2. Don't you think that perhaps after all the professors and the faculty and the exam-

iners and all the rest of the crabbed machinery of your daily toil is something striving for your good? Dip deep your pen in your Christmas ink, my boy, and overstate the truth for your soul's good.

3. Are you not going some day, when your college years are long since past, and when the poor fretful thing that is called practical life has caught you in its toils and carries you onwards towards your last Christmas,—are you not going to look back at them through the soft haze of recollection, as to the memory of a shaded caravansary in a long and weary pilgrimage?

IDLENESS: A SONG FOR THE LONG VACATION

Idleness: A Song for the Long Vacation

LET me sing a song of summer, when the
    college days are done,
  In the drowsy long vacation under-
    neath the torrid sun,
Let me summarize the knowledge that the stu-
  dent gains at college,
Let me sing to you the Vanity of Life.
Let me lie among the daisies, with my stomach
  to the sky,
Making poses in the roses, in the middle of
  July,
Let me nestle in the nettles, let me there ab-
  sorb the dew
On a pair of flannel breeches with the stitches
  worked in blue.
Let me set me,
Just to pet me,

Where the college cannot get me,
Won't you let me, Oh, yes, do!

Let me sing to you the Nothingness, the Van-
ity of Life,
Let me teach you of the effort you should shirk,
Let me show you that you never ought to make
the least endeavour,
Or indulge yourself in any kind of work.

You never ought to tire yourself with trying
to be good,
Or to waste yourself with wishing to be wise,
For a man of low capacity whose head is made
of wood,
Never, never can be clever if he tries.

Oh, the Wickedness of Working, and the Sin
of being Strong,
Oh, the folly of distinguishing between the
Right and Wrong,
Oh, the Evilness of Effort, and the Sorrow of
Succeeding,
Oh, the Risk of early Rising and the Shame
of Underfeeding;—

Oh, there's nothing in sincerity,
And aspiration's bad,
Asperity, austerity,
Are nothing but a fad,
Morality and charity,
Are only for the sick,
Fixed conviction,
Earnest Diction,
Merely Rhetoric:—
Piety,
Sobriety,
All of that I vow
Is just a lot
Of Tommy Rot
That won't do now:—

When the Politicians' Politics are written out
    in ink,
And their true convictions set in black and
    white,
Then a chemical analysis of what they really
    think
Would leave nothing but a vacuum in sight.

'Tis the standing proposition of an honest
    opposition
A perpetual corruption to imply,
And the steady obligation of a just admin-
    istration
To consider every statement is a lie.

When the Orator enrages in a speech of fifty
    pages,
He does not really mean to use a gun,
When the candidate enlarges on the vigour
    of his charges
It is only just his little bit of fun.

Oh, there's nothing on the platform,
And there's nothing in the press,
Give it this or that form,
It's neither more nor less,
Liquified loquacity,
Ink in torrents shed,
Copious Mendacity,
But really nothing said.

When the business man is busy with the buzzing
    of his brain
And his mind is set on bonds and stocks and
    shares,
While he's building up the country with his
    utmost might and main,
Do you think it's for the country that he cares?

When he's making us a railroad, when he's
    digging us a mine
Every philanthropic benefit he flaunts,
When he says that he has blest us with his
    output of asbestos
It is nothing but our money that he wants.

Why bother then to fake it, why not knock us
    down and take it?
Let the jobber be a robber if he must,
Let the banker tell the teller to go down into
    the cellar,
And then hash the cash and swear the bank
    is bust.

Oh, there's only Sin in Syndicates,
And who can trust a Trust
The Golden Cloth
Conceals the Moth
And cankers into Rust.
The truly wise
Will lift his eyes
Towards a higher goal,
Will steal a pile
That's worth the while
And get out whole.

Then gather in the meadows all, as quickly as
you can,
The pompous politician and the bulky business
man,
Let the lawyer in the lilies lie becalmed in statu
quo,
And the broker break off broking just for half
an hour or so:

Let the politician prattle to the periwinkle
blue,
Covered over with the clover let him play
at Peek-a-boo,

Let the clergy in the cowslips cuddle down
    and double up,
And there imbibe the buttermilk from out
    the buttercup.

      Let us gambol
      Let us ramble
      O'er the flower embowered lea
      O'er the meadow
      In the shadow
      Of the elderberry tree
      Let us dress us,
      As may bless us,
      With no public there to see,
      Care not which is
      Proper breeches
      For a summer negligee.
      Or array us
      To display us
      In a pair of flannel pants,
      Taking chances
      On advances
      From the enterprising ants.

Then at even
When the heaven
Reddens to the western sky
All together
In the heather
Sing a summer
        Lullaby.

THE DIVERSIONS OF A PRO-FESSOR OF HISTORY

The Diversions of a Professor of History

IN my earlier days of college teaching, I was for a time, under the sharp spur of necessity, a professor of history. I expected at that period that my researches in this capacity would add much to our knowledge of the known globe. They did not. But they at least enabled me to survive the financial strain of the long vacation by writing historical poetry for the press.

The little verses which here follow were written day by day and appeared here and there in the forgotten corners of odd newspapers. They occasioned about as much interest or illumination as a firefly at mid-day.

It will be noted that I used up only the month of August. Any professor of history in the same need as I was may have all the other eleven months.

I called the verses—

TO-DAY IN HISTORY

August 4, 1778

(Victory of Gwalior)

Oh, the neglected education
Of this poor young Canadian nation
To think that you never heard before
Of the wonderful victory of Gwalior
   How the British suffered with heat and thirst
   And they curst
   Their worst
   Till they nearly burst
And then in the end came out victorious.
Oh! wasn't the whole thing Gwaliorious.

August 2, 1704

(BATTLE OF BLENHEIM)

This was the very occasion when,
Great Marlborough gained the battle of Blen—
   The rest of the noble word won't rhyme
   Say it in silence or call it "heim."
   On the very same spot
   In other years
   Old Caspar shed his senile tears
   And the reason was
   If you ask me why
   Because his father was "forced to fly!"
   Oh, poor old Caspar you really ought,
   To have lived in the age of the aeronaut.

August 5, 1809

(Birth of Alfred Tennyson)

On this very day
At early morn
Lord Alfred Tennyson chanced to be born.
Had it not been so, I really hate,
To think of the poor elocutionist's fate.
  He couldn't have been
  The sad May Queen,
  He couldn't have brayed
  The light Brigade
  To a ten cent audience (half afraid,
  When he hitches
  His breeches
  With soldier-like twitches
  To shew how the Russians were killed in the
      ditches).
  He never could shake
  With emotion and make
  The price of a meal with his 'Break, Break,
      Break.'
              Alas, poor bloke,
        He'd be broke, broke, broke.

August 8, 1843

(THE ANNEXATION OF NATAL)

When we in touch with heathens come,
We send them first a case of rum,
Next, to rebuke their native sin,
We send a missionary in:
Then when the hungry Hottentot
Has boiled his pastor in a pot,
We teach him Christian, dumb contrition,
By means of dum-dum ammunition,
　The situation grows perplexed,
　The wicked country is annexed:
But, oh! the change when o'er the wild,
Our sweet Humanity has smiled!
The savage shaves his shaggy locks,
Wears breeches and balbriggan socks,
Learns Euclid, classifies the fossils,
Draws pictures of the Twelve Apostles,
And now his pastor at the most,
He is content simply to roast:
　Forgetful of the art of war,
　He smokes a twenty cent cigar,

He drinks not rum, his present care is
For whisky and Apollinaris.
Content for this his land to change,
He fattens up and dies of mange.
　　Lo! on the ashes of his Kraal,
　　A Protestant Ca-the-der-al!

August 9, 1902

(KING EDWARD VII CROWNED)

Again the changing year shall bring
The Coronation of a King,
While yet the reign seemed but begun,
The sceptre passes to the son.
  Oh! little, little round of life,
  Where each must walk the selfsame way,
  Oh, little fever-fret and strife
  That passes into yesterday
  When each at last, with struggling breath,
  Clasps in the dark the hand of Death.
    Oh! Sorrow of our Common Lot,
    Go, mark it well, and Envy not.

August 10, 1866

(THE STRAITS SETTLEMENTS FOUNDED)

Tell me now, will you please relate,
Why do they call these Settlements straight?
    Does it mean to say
    That the gay
    Malay
    Is too moral to quarrel
    In any way?
    Does he never fight
    On a Saturday night,
    When he's drunk in his junk
    And his heart is light?

Have they got no music, no whisky, no ladies?
Well—it may be straight, but it's gloomy as
    Hades.

August 12, 1905

(Anglo-Japanese Alliance)

"Valiant, noble Japanee,
Listen to Britannia's plea,
Since the battle of Yalu,
I've been yearning all for you;
Since the fight at Meter Hill
Other suitors make me ill;
Tell me not of German beaux
Addle-headed, adipose,
Double-barreled Dutchman plain,
Sullen, sombre sons of Spain,
Flaxen Swede, Roumanian red,
Fickle Frenchmen, underfed,
  Nay, I care for none of these,
  Take me, Oh, my Japanese,
Yamagata, you of Yeddo,
Fold me, hold me to your heart
Togo, take me to Tokio,

143

Tell me not that we must part;
   In your home at Nagasaki
   Cuddle me against your khaki,
Since the Russians couldn't tan you,
Rule, I pray you, rule Britannia!

August 14, 1763

(Admiral Albemarle Took Havana)

On a critical day,
In those awful wars,
The fleet, they say,
Ran out of cigars;
It sounds like a nightmare, a dream, a bogie,
They hadn't even a Pittsburg stogie,
Nor a single plug,
Of the noble drug,
And from vessel to vessel the signal flew
"Our sailors are dying for want of a chew."

From boyhood up those sailors had been
Preserved and pickled in nicotine
By conscientious smoking and drinking
They had kept themselves from the horror of
thinking.

Then Admiral Albemarle looked to leeward
And summoned in haste his bedroom steward,

And said, "My hearty, just cast your eyes on
The sou' sou' west, and skin the horizon,
That cloud of smoke and that fort and ban-
    ner?"
The sailor answered, "That place is Havana."
Within a second or even a fraction
The Admiral summoned the ships to action,
The signal was read by every tar,
"You hit a Spaniard and get a cigar."

Nor need I say to readers who smoke
How the furious burst of artillery broke,
How they shot at Havana, bombarded and
    shook it
And so as a matter of course they took it.
   The terms of surrender were brief but witty,
"We'll take the cigars, you can keep the city."

August 11, 1535

(JACQUES CARTIER DISCOVERED THE
ST. LAWRENCE)

This is the day
When Cartier
Came sailing up to the Saguenay.
He found the St. Lawrence
Without a chart.
Oh, wasn't Cart
 Exceedingly smart!

August 15, 1870

(Manitoba Becomes a Province)

Now everybody, drunk or sober,
Sing loud the praise of Manitoba;
Throw back your head, inflate your chest,
And sing the glories of the West;
Sing, without slackening or stop,
The jubilation of the crop;
Sing of the bending ear of wheat,
That stands at least some fourteen feet;
And soft its tasselled head inclines,
To flirt with the potato vines;
Sing of the prairie covered over,
With cabbage trees and shrubs of clover;
While English settlers lose their way,
In forests of gigantic hay.

How wonderful be it confessed,
The passing of the bygone West;
The painted Indian rides no more,
He stands—at a tobacco store;
His cruel face proclaims afar
The terror of the cheap cigar,

148

Behold his once downtrodden squaw;
Protected by provincial law;
Their tee-pee has become—Oh, gee,
A station on the G. T. P.,
And on the scenes of Ancient War,
Thy rails I. C. O. C. P. R.

August 16, 1713

(New Brunswick Founded)

I need not sing your praises, every word
Of mine, New Brunswick, would appear absurd,
Beside the melody that freely pours
From out these polysyllables of yours.
  Where Chedabudcto roars and bold Buc-
     touche
  Rivals the ripples of the Restigouche;
  Or where beneath its ancient British flag
  Aroostook faces Mettawamkeag.
  Oh, fairy-land of meadow, vale and brook
  Kennebekasis, Chiputneticook,
  Shick-Shock and Shediac, Point Escuminac
  Miramachi and Peticodiac.
    This is no place to try poetic wit,
     I guess at least I know enough to quit.

August 17, 1896

(Gold Discovered in the Yukon)

This is the day
In a climate cold
They found that wretched thing called Gold;
That miserable, hateful stuff,
How can I curse at it enough,
That foul, deceitful, meretricious,
Abominable, avaricious,
That execrable, bought and sold
Commodity that men call gold.
How can I find the words to state it,
The deep contempt with which I hate it;
I charge you, nay, I here command it,
Give it me not, I could not stand it:
You hear me shout, you mark me holler?
Don't dare to offer me a dollar.
The mere idea of taking it,
Gives me an epileptic fit.
What use is Gold?
Alas, poor dross,
That brings but sorrow, pain and loss,

What after all the use of riches?
'Twill buy fine clothes and velvet breeches,
Stone houses, pictures, motor cars,
Roast quail on toast and large cigars,
But, oh, my friends, will this compare
With a fresh draught of mountain air?
Will wretched viands such as these
Compare with simple bread and cheese?
  Nay, let me to my bosom press
  The gastronomic watercress,
  And hug within my diaphragm
  The spoon of thimbleberry jam,
  And while the wicked wine I spurn,
  Quaff deep the wholesome mountain burn,
  The simple life, the harmless drink
  Is good enough,—I do not think.

August 18, 1577

(BIRTH OF RUBENS)

Think it not idle affectation
If I express my admiration
Of frescoes, canvases and plasters
In short, the work of Ancient Masters.
  You take a man like Botticelli,
  Or the Italian Vermicelli,
  Rubens and Titian, Angelo,
  Anheuser Busch, Sapolio,
  John P. Velasquez and Murillo,
  Fra Lippo Lipp, Buffalo Billo,
  Pilsener Lager and Giotto;
  Admire them! Why, you've simply got to;
What if you do not understand
Just the idea they had in hand,
What if they do not quite convey
The meaning that they should portray?
What if you don't exactly find
A purpose in them, never mind,
Beneath the coat of gathered dust
Take the great geniuses on trust.

If you should see in public places
Fat cherubs whose expansive faces
Wear a strong anti-temperance air
The work is Rubens, you may swear;
Fat ladies in inclined position
You always may ascribe to Titian,
While simple love scenes in a grotto,
Betray the master hand of Giotto.
But if you doubt, do not enquire,
Fall into ecstasies, admire,
Stare at the picture, deeply peer
And murmur, "What an atmosphere";
And if your praises never tire
No one will know you are a liar.

August 19, 1897

(INTRODUCTION OF THE HORSELESS CAB)

Farewell, a long farewell, Old Friend,
'Tis the beginning of the end.
So there you stand, poor patient brute,
Dressed in your little leather suit;
Your harness, buckles, straps and bows
An outline parody of clothes.
Speechless, confined, without volition,
It seems to me that your position,
Is with a subtle meaning rife,—
A queer analogy of life.
A depth of meaning underlies
Those blinkers that restrain your eyes;
I see a melancholy omen
In straps that cramp your poor abdomen,
I could supply, would it avail,
Sad speculations on your tail
So docked that, swishing at the fleas,
Its arc is only nine degrees;
But more than all, I seem to trace
Analogies in your long face,

So utterly devoid of humour,
Long ears that hearken every rumour,
A sweeping snout, protruding teeth,
And chinless underlip beneath;
So joyless and so serious
Well may your features weary us.
For musing thus, I think perhaps
Your life is ours, the little straps
The shafts that hold us to the track
The burden ever on the back,—

Enough, the theme is old, of course,
I am an ass, you are a horse.

August 20, 1896

(FRIDTJOF NANSEN'S SHIP "THE FRAM"
RETURNS SAFELY TO SKJERVOE)

What a glorious day
For old Norway,
When the *Fram* came sailing into the Bay
To the dear old fjord,
With its crew on bjord
All safely restjord
By the hand of the Ljord;
   And they shouted "Whoe
     Is this Skjervoe?"
   'And they rent the ajer with a loud Hulljoe;
    While the crowd, on skis
       As thick as biis
       Slid down
       To the town
       On their hands and kniis.
And oh! what cries
When they recognise
     A man with a pair of sealskin pants on
     'And thjere, I decljare, is Fridtjof Nan-
        sen.

157

August 22, 1903

(EXPEDITION OF THE "NEPTUNE" UNDER
COMMANDER LOW TO HUDSON STRAITS)

While we welter
In the swelter
Of the pestilential Heat
Drinking Sodas
In Pagodas
At the Corner of the Street
      It seems to me
      That it would be
      My highest aspiration
      To sail away
      On a Holiday
      Of Arctic exploration.

Let me lie in my pyjamas on the ice of Baffin's
    Bay,
In the thinnest of chemises where the Polar
    breezes play,
Underneath a frozen awning let me lie at ease
    a span,
While beneath the bright Aurora roars the
    ventilation fan.

Can you wonder now that Nansen and that
     Peary, and that Low,
Should wander forth,
And struggle North,
As far as they can go?
When the hero
Under Zero
Lives on frozen lager beer,
And a demi-can
Of Pemmican
You need not shed a tear.
He seeks a higher latitude,
I quite admit the feat;
The reason is a platitude,
He's crazy with the heat.

August 26, 1346

(Great Slaughter of the French by the
English at Crecy)

How strange it seems to me that even then
Man raised his hand against his fellow men,
Fretful and eager, still his mind he bent
New engines of destruction to invent.

Poor little Creature, through his whole life
story
Waving his little flag and shouting Glory.
Vexing his puny strength and panting breath
Merely to hasten ever-certain Death.

August 27, 1870

(INVENTION OF THE GRAMOPHONE)

I freely admit that the gay gramophone,
Possesses attractions entirely its own,
I frankly concede that the wonders of science
Are seen at their best in that very appliance;
And yet notwithstanding, I deeply deplore
The gramophone owned by the Joneses next
    door.
I rise in the morning, the first thing I hear
Is "Sleep on, my Darling, for Mother is near,"
I sit down to breakfast and hear with surprise
A loud invitation to Drink with Mine Eyes.
I come from my office, the gramophone's strain
Informs me that Johnnie has marched home
    again.
I sit down to read but the minute I do so
The Joneses arouse a carouse with Caruso,
Their strains all the veins of my cerebrum clog,
My slumbers their numbers monotonous dog,
Will nothing but homicide end or prevent it,
Oh, Edison, why did you ever invent it?

THE OLD COLLEGE AND THE
NEW UNIVERSITY

The Old College and the New University [1]

I HAVE it on tradition that in the year 1860 or thereabouts the way in which a student matriculated into a college was, that the venerable gentleman named the Principal called him into his office and asked him who his father was, and whether he had read Virgil.

If the old gentleman liked the answers to these questions, he let the boy in.

Nowadays when a student matriculates, it requires in the first place some four pages of printed regulations to tell him how; after which there is demanded two weeks of continuous writing, and the consumption of at least twenty square yards of writing paper.

One of these two systems is what we now call Organisation; the other is not. I dare not

[1] Written for the McGill Annual of 1923.

doubt for a minute which is the best. There is the same difference as there is between a Court Martial and an Appeal to the Privy Council, so that it would be folly, if not treason, to express a preference for the older plan.

But like many other things the plan was not wholly bad. For they do say that sometimes the venerable Principal would keep the boy talking for half an hour or so, and when the youth left, he would say, "Remarkable boy, that! Has the makings of a scholar in him!" And the little matriculant, his heart swollen with pride, would hurry away to the college library with a new fever for Virgil's Æneid burning within him. By such and similar processes there was set up in the college a sort of personal relationship, not easily established nowadays even by the "contact" section of the "Committee on Friendliness."

For nowadays every matriculant is just a name and a number, and when he gets to the first year he is merely a "case," and in his second year simply a "seat," and in his third year a "condition," and in his fourth year, at the best, a "parchment," and after that not even a memory.

There can, of course, be no doubt that present days and present things are better—none whatever. To anybody who attended a place that was called a "college" and had three hundred students, it is wonderful to come back and find it grown—or at any rate swollen, inflated, shall I say?—into a University of three thousand students with a President instead of a Principal, and with as many "faculties" and departments and committees as there are in the League of Nations. It is wonderful to think of this vast organisation pouring out its graduates like beans out of a hopper. It is marvellous, I repeat, to reflect on the way that everything is organised, standardised, unified, and reduced to a provable sample of excellence.

The college athletics of the older day, how feeble they seem by comparison now. The group of students gathered round the campus in the October dusk to cheer the football team —each cheering, or calling, upon some poor notion of his own as to the merits of the play

—how crude it seems beside the organised hysteria of the Rooters' Club. The college daily journal of to-day, with its seven columns of real "news," and needing nothing but a little murder to put it right in line with the big one-cent papers, the organs of one-cent opinion,— how greatly superior it is to the old time "College Journal." That poor maundering thing made its appearance at irregular intervals, emerging feebly like the Arctic sun from behind its cloud of debt, and containing nothing later in the way of "news" than a disquisition on the art of William Shakespeare.

Or take the college library of the old days, how limited it was with its one ancient librarian, with a beard that reached his girdle, handing out the books one by one, and remembering the students by their faces. As if up-to-date students had any!—

The old college is no doubt gone and we could not bring it back if we would. But it would perhaps be well for us if we could keep alive something of the intimate and friendly spirit that inspired it.

Whereupon, I am certain, some one will at once propose a University committee on brotherly love with power to compel attendance and impose fines.

THE END